Nursery Rhymes

This book belongs to:

....

Hey Diddle Diddle

Hey diddle diddle,

The cat and the fiddle,

The cow jumped over the moon.

The little dog laughed

To see such fun,

And the dish ran away

With the spoon.

Twinkle Twinkle, Little Star

Twinkle twinkle, little star,
How I wonder what you are.
Up above the world so high,
Like a diamond in the sky.
Twinkle twinkle, little star,
How I wonder what you are.

Mary Mary, Quite Contrary

Mary Mary, quite contrary,
How does your garden grow?
With silver bells and cockleshells,
And pretty maids all in a row.

Hickory Dickory Dock

Hickory dickory dock,
The mouse ran up the clock.
The clock struck one,
The mouse ran down,
Hickory dickory dock.

Little Jack Horner

Little Jack Horner sat in a corner,

Eating a Christmas pie.

He stuck in his thumb,

And pulled out a plum,

And said, "What a good boy am I!"

The Queen of Hearts

The Queen of Hearts
She made some tarts,
All on a summer's day.
The Knave of Hearts,
He stole the tarts,
And took them clean away.

The King of Hearts
Called for the tarts,
And beat the Knave full sore.
The Knave of Hearts
Brought back the tarts,
And vowed he'd steal no more.

Little Bo Peep

Little Bo Peep has lost her sheep,
And doesn't know where to find them.
Leave them alone,
And they'll come home,
Wagging their tails behind them.

Little Miss Muffet

Little Miss Muffet sat on a tuffet,
Eating her curds and whey.
Along came a spider,
Who sat down beside her
And frightened Miss Muffet away.

This Little Piggy

This little piggy went to market,

This little piggy stayed home.

This little piggy had roast beef,

This little piggy had none.

This little piggy cried,

"Wee wee wee wee!" all the way home.

Rock-a-bye Baby

Rock-a-bye baby, on the tree top.
When the wind blows, the cradle will rock,
When the bough breaks, the cradle will fall,
Down will come baby, cradle and all.

Here We Go Round the Mulberry Bush

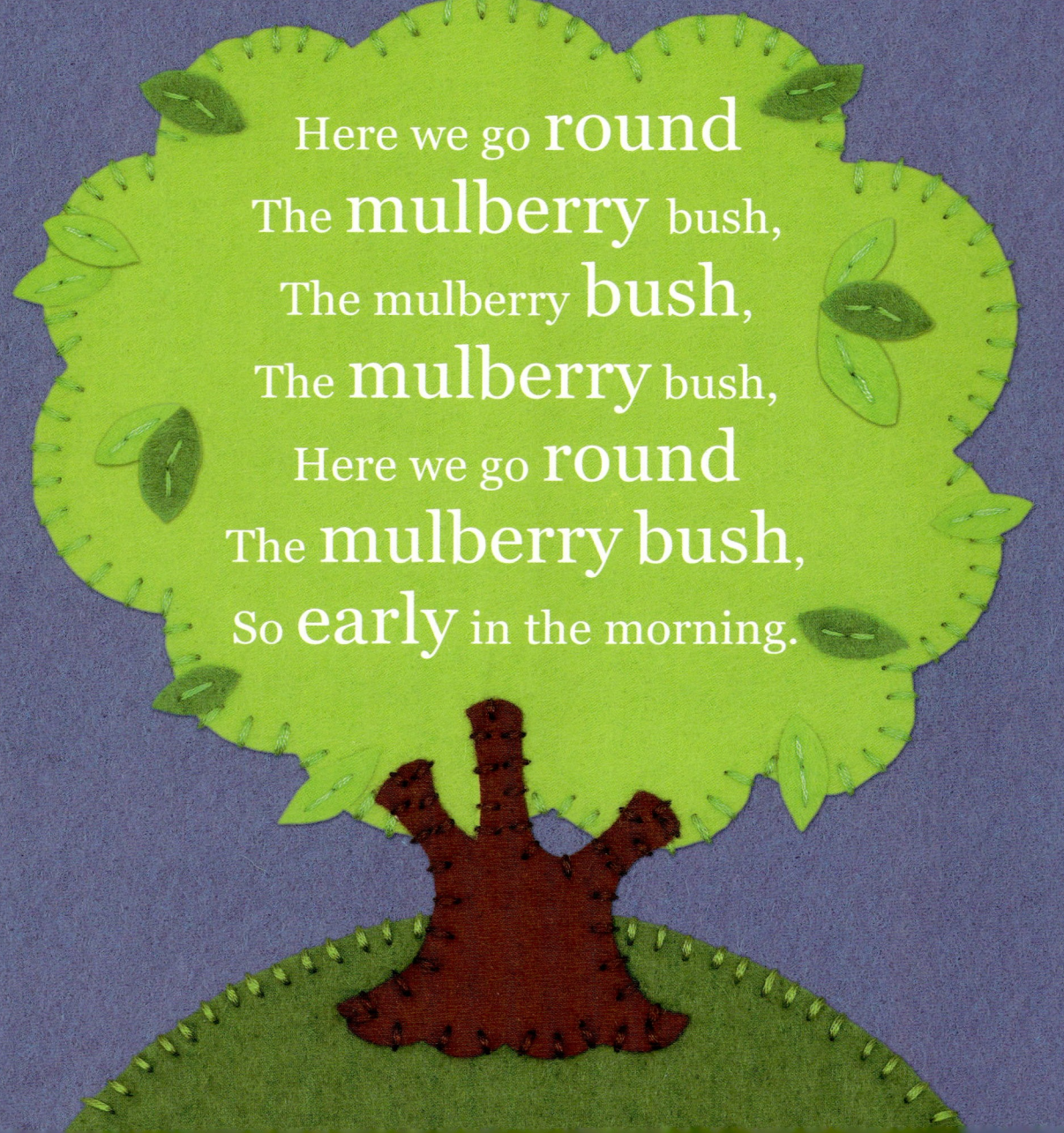

Here we go round
The mulberry bush,
The mulberry bush,
The mulberry bush,
Here we go round
The mulberry bush,
So early in the morning.

Old Mother Hubbard

Old Mother Hubbard went to the cupboard,

To get her poor dog a bone.

But when she got there,

The cupboard was bare,

And so the poor dog had none.

Pat-a-cake, Pat-a-cake

Pat-a-cake, pat-a-cake, baker's man!
Bake me a cake as fast as you can.
Pat it and prick it, and mark it with B,
Put it in the oven for baby and me.

Yankee Doodle

Yankee Doodle came to town,
Riding on a pony,
Stuck a feather in his hat
And called it macaroni.

Jack and Jill

Jack and Jill went up the hill,
To fetch a pail of water.
Jack fell down and broke his crown
And Jill came tumbling after.

Humpty Dumpty

Humpty Dumpty sat on a wall,
Humpty Dumpty had a great fall.
All the King's horses and all the King's men,
Couldn't put Humpty together again.

Sing a Song of Sixpence

Sing a song of sixpence,
A pocketful of rye.
Four-and-twenty blackbirds
Baked in a pie.

When the **pie** was **opened,**
The **birds** began to sing,
Was not that a **dainty dish**
To set before the **King?**

Pussy Cat, Pussy Cat

Pussy cat, pussy cat, where have you been?
I've been to London to visit the Queen.
Pussy cat, pussy cat, what did you there?
I frightened a little mouse under her chair.

Baa Baa, Black Sheep

Baa baa, black sheep, have you any wool?
Yes sir, yes sir, three bags full.
One for the master, one for the dame,
And one for the little boy who lives down the lane.

Three Little Kittens

Three little kittens lost their mittens,
And they began to cry,
"Oh mother dear, we sadly fear
Our mittens we have lost."
"What? Lost your mittens?
You naughty kittens!
Then you shall have no pie."
"Meow, meow, meow."

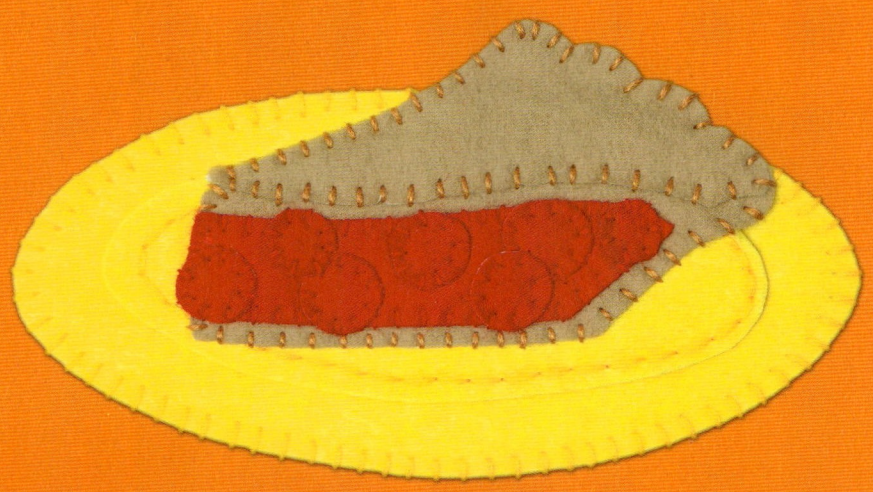

The three little kittens found their mittens,
And they began to cry,
"Oh mother dear, see here, see here,
Our mittens we have found."
"What? Found your mittens?
You good little kittens!
Then you shall have some pie."
"Purr, purr, purr!"

There Was an Old Woman

There was an old woman who lived in a shoe,
She had so many children, she didn't know what to do.
She gave them some broth without any bread,
Then whipped them all soundly and put them to bed.

Goosey Goosey Gander

Goosey Goosey Gander, whither shall I wander?
Upstairs and downstairs and in my lady's chamber.
There I met an old man who would not say his prayers,
I took him by the left leg and threw him down the stairs.